SRa

Specific Skill Series

Identifying Inferences

William H. Wittenberg

Fifth Edition

SRa ®

SRA/McGraw-Hill

Columbus, Ohio

Cover, Back Cover, John Downer/Masterfile

SRA/McGraw-Hill

*A Division of The **McGraw·Hill** Companies*

Printed in the United States of America.

Send all inquiries to:
    SRA/McGraw-Hill
    8787 Orion Place
    Columbus, OH 43240-4027

ISBN 0-02-687999-9

    5 6 7 IPC 03 02 01

To the Teacher

PURPOSE:
IDENTIFYING INFERENCES is designed to develop one of the most difficult interpretive skills—arriving at a *probable* conclusion from a limited amount of information. IDENTIFYING INFERENCES requires the readers to *read between the lines*. They must utilize previously acquired knowledge and past experiences in order to fully comprehend the message of the text.

FOR WHOM:
The skill of IDENTIFYING INFERENCES is developed through a series of books spanning ten levels (Picture, Preparatory, A, B, C, D, E, F, G, H). The Picture Level is for pupils who have not acquired a basic sight vocabulary. The Preparatory Level is for pupils who have a basic sight vocabulary but are not yet ready for the first-grade-level book. Books A through H are appropriate for pupils who can read on levels one through eight, respectively. **The use of the *Specific Skill Series Placement Test* is recommended to determine the appropriate level.**

THE NEW EDITION:
The fifth edition of the *Specific Skill Series* maintains the quality and focus that has distinguished this program for more than 25 years. A key element central to the program's success has been the unique nature of the reading selections. Nonfiction pieces about current topics have been designed to stimulate the interest of students, motivating them to use the comprehension strategies they have learned to further their reading. To keep this important aspect of the program intact, a percentage of the reading selections have been replaced in order to ensure the continued relevance of the subject material.

In addition, a significant percentage of the artwork in the program has been replaced to give the books a contemporary look. The cover photographs are designed to appeal to readers of all ages.

SESSIONS:
Short practice sessions are the most effective. It is desirable to have a practice session every day or every other day, using a few units each session.

SCORING:
Pupils should record their answers on the reproducible worksheets. The worksheets make scoring easier and provide uniform records of the pupils' work. Using worksheets also avoids consuming the exercise books.

To the Teacher

It is important for pupils to know how well they are doing. For this reason, units should be scored as soon as they have been completed. Then a discussion can be held in which pupils justify their choices. (The Integrated Language Activities, many of which are open-ended, do not lend themselves to an objective score; thus there are no answer keys for these pages.)

GENERAL INFORMATION ON *IDENTIFYING INFERENCES:*

The difference between a *conclusion* and an *inference*, as presented in this series, is that a conclusion is a logical deduction based upon conclusive evidence, while an inference is an "educated guess" based upon evidence that is less than conclusive. Read this sample:

> Captain Fujihara quickly parked the fire truck, grabbed his helmet, and rushed into the house at 615 Oak Street.

You can *conclude* that Captain Fujihara knows how to drive because that ability was required to park the fire truck. You can *infer* that there is a fire at 615 Oak Street because Captain Fujihara took his helmet and rushed into that house. This is an inference because firefighters do rush to put out fires. It is an inference because there may be another reason for the firefighter's rushing to the house. Captain Fujihara may live there and be late for supper. Thus an inference is supported by evidence, but the evidence is not necessarily conclusive.

SUGGESTED STEPS:

1. Pupils read the text. On levels C-H, after reading, pupils examine the statements that follow the text to determine whether each is a factually true statement (T), a false statement (F), or a valid inference (I). ("True" statements are those about which the reader can be *certain* from the text.) On lower levels, pupils determine which statement about the text or picture is probably true.
2. Then pupils reexamine the text or picture for evidence to support their decisions.
3. Pupils record their answers on the worksheets.

RELATED MATERIALS:

Specific Skill Series Placement Tests, which enable the teacher to place pupils at their appropriate levels in each skill, are available for the Elementary (Pre-1–6) and Midway (4–8) grade levels.

About This Book

What do you do when you look at a picture? Do you just look at what the picture shows? Or do you think about other things the picture might be telling you? When you look at a picture of a boy petting a dog, you may think something like this: He probably likes the dog. When you make a guess like this, you are making an **inference**.

A picture shows you some things. Often, you can guess about other things the picture does not show. When you see a picture of a girl diving into a pool, you can guess that she knows how to swim. How do you know this? You know from what you yourself have seen and done. An inference is a guess you make from what is shown *plus* what you know.

In this book, you will look at a picture. Think about what the picture shows. Think about what else is probably true. Then listen to two sentences. One sentence will not be true. The other sentence will be a guess that you can make about the picture. It will say something that is *probably* true. Choose the sentence that is probably true.

Which is probably true?

(A) **Soon it will snow.**

(B) **The boy and girl like to play ball.**

Which is probably true?

(A) The boy has many friends.

(B) The boy can ride a bike.

Which is probably true?

(A) The girl likes to read.

(B) The girl can run fast.

Which is probably true?

(A) The dog likes to play with Mother.

(B) Mother will not be happy.

Which is probably true?

(A) The boy can read.

(B) The book is about animals.

Which is probably true?

(A) **The girl has a big boat.**

(B) **The girl likes to fish.**

Which is probably true?

(A) The bike can't go fast.

(B) The boy has a new bike.

Which is probably true?

(A) **The boy likes the cake.**

(B) **Mother found the cake.**

Which is probably true?

(A) There is no school today.

(B) The girl likes to go to school.

Which is probably true?

(A) The woman is not happy.

(B) The woman wants to eat.

Which is probably true?

(A) **The boy wants a new pet.**

(B) **The boy will be surprised.**

Which is probably true?

(A) **The dog wants to eat.**

(B) **The man does not like the dog.**

A. Exercising Your Skill

Look at the picture of the girl winning a medal. Then read the lists. In each list, two of the things belong. One thing does not belong. Write the headings on your paper. Then write the words that belong under each heading.

How the Girl Felt

happy

proud

sad

Why the Girl Won

She was slow.

She practiced hard.

She was fast.

B. Expanding Your Skill

In order to play some sports you need to go to a special place. Other sports you can play almost anywhere. Put each sport under the right heading. Write on your paper.

| running | skiing | biking | swimming |

| Sports to play in special places | Sports to play almost anywhere |

C. Exploring Language

Draw a picture of the girl who won wearing her medal. Then copy the story below on your paper. Use your own words to fill in the blanks.

The girl won the ___ . She ran very ___ . The other runners ran ___ than the girl. The girl felt ___ when she won the race.

D. Expressing Yourself

Do one of these things.

1. Tell your classmates what sport you would like to win a medal for someday. Tell why.

2. Draw a picture of yourself practicing your favorite sport.

Which is probably true?

    (A) The girl is going to jump.

    (B) The girl likes to go fast.

Which is probably true?

(A) **It is cold out.**

(B) **The girl will play ball.**

Which is probably true?

(A) The cat can open the door.

(B) The cat does not like the rain.

Which is probably true?

(A) Father can't swim.

(B) The boy is learning to swim.

Which is probably true?

(A) **The girl likes to make things.**

(B) **The girl does not like to fly.**

Which is probably true?

(A) **The boy will have fun.**

(B) **The boy is not happy.**

Which is probably true?

   (A) The girl can ride a bike.
   (B) The girl lost her bike.

Which is probably true?

(A) **The girl wants to sleep.**

(B) **The girl has cold feet.**

Which is probably true?

(A) The man does not know Father.

(B) Father and the man are friends.

Which is probably true?

(A) The girl will ride.
(B) The horse will eat now.

Which is probably true?

(A) **Father can't fix the TV.**

(B) **Father has a new TV.**

Which is probably true?

(A) **The girl likes to swim.**

(B) **The girl made the boat.**

A. Exercising Your Skill

Look at the picture below. Where do you think the boy is? Think about your visits to the dentist and doctor. Then complete the lists below. Use your own paper.

Reasons to Visit the Dentist

_____

_____

_____

Reasons to Visit the Doctor

_____

_____

_____

B. Expanding Your Skill

Talk about the picture.

- What is happening in the picture?
- Why is the boy holding his face?
- How is the boy feeling?
- Who will help the boy?
- Will the boy feel better next week?

C. Exploring Language

Look at the picture of the boy at the dentist. Copy the story below on your paper. Use your own words to fill in the blanks.

> The boy is feeling very ____ . He has a sore ____ . His dad took him to the ____ . The boy hopes the dentist will make his tooth stop ____ .

D. Expressing Yourself

Do one of these things.

1. Draw a picture of the first time you visited the dentist. Tell your classmates how you felt when you were there.

2. Write a story about what the Tooth Fairy does with all the baby teeth she collects.

Which is probably true?

(A) **The girl has no friends.**

(B) **The girl wants to play.**

Which is probably true?

(A) **The girl wants to stop.**

(B) **The girl likes to ride.**

Which is probably true?

(A) **The man is lost.**

(B) **The man is by his house.**

Which is probably true?

(A) **The girl has a pet.**

(B) **The dog has a funny name.**

Which is probably true?

(A) **Mother is angry.**

(B) **The girl likes to sail.**

Which is probably true?

(A) The man likes to walk.

(B) The car can't run.

Which is probably true?

(A) It's going to rain.

(B) It's time to eat.

Which is probably true?

(A) The woman does not like to fly.

(B) It's a trick.

Which is probably true?

(A) **The pig has nothing to eat.**

(B) **The pig likes to eat.**

Which is probably true?

    (A) The boy will climb the tree.

    (B) The boy lives in the tree.

DOCTOR

Which is probably true?

(A) The girl is going to work.

(B) The girl does not feel well.

Which is probably true?

(A) **The tree will be cut down.**

(B) **The road is old.**

Which is probably true?

(A) People like the park.

(B) The park is not open at night.

Which is probably true?

(A) The boy lives next door.

(B) The girl is a good player.

A. Exercising Your Skill

Look at the picture below. Think about parks you have seen. Then complete the list below. Write on your paper.

Fun Things to Do at a Park

_____

_____

_____

B. Expanding Your Skill

Pick the words from the box that tell about things at a park. Write them on your paper.

grass	train	television
whale	benches	swings

C. Exploring Language

Draw a picture of your favorite thing to do at a park. Give your drawing a name. Write the name on your drawing. Then copy the story to tell about your favorite thing. Use your own words to fill in the blanks.

My Favorite Thing to Do at a Park

My favorite thing to do at a park is ____ . It makes me feel ____ to do it. Other people may feel this way at a park. I can tell from the way they ____ .

D. Expressing Yourself

With a friend, pretend that you are building a park for children. Write a list of all the places and things you would put in the park. Remember to think of things that are made and things that grow. Draw a plan of your park to share with your classmates.

Which is probably true?

    (A) The man likes to look at TV.

    (B) The man is not going to work today.

Which is probably true?

(A) The girl likes to go high.

(B) The boat is going slow.

Which is probably true?

(A) **The girl will eat now.**

(B) **The girl has a pet bird.**

Which is probably true?

(A) **The baby can swim.**

(B) **It's a hot day.**

Which is probably true?

(A) There will be no school today.

(B) It's a good day for walking.

Which is probably true?

(A) **The baby wants to eat.**

(B) **The baby can walk.**

Which is probably true?

(A) The girl can't go out to ride her bike.

(B) Water will come into the house.

Which is probably true?

(A) The water is hot.

(B) The boy can't stop.

Which is probably true?

(A) The cat has no home.

(B) The dog is too slow.

Which is probably true?

(A) **The girl likes to run.**

(B) **The girl wants to sleep.**

Which is probably true?

(A) The boy is a very good player.

(B) The man knows how to play.

Which is probably true?

(A) The girls can't swim.

(B) The dog does not like the water.

A. Exercising Your Skill

Look at the picture of the boy roller-skating. Then complete the lists next to the picture. Write on your paper.

How
the Boy Feels

_____

_____

_____

What the Boy
Needs to Practice

_____

_____

_____

B. Expanding Your Skill

There are some things that everyone learns how to do as a baby. Other things take lots of practice. From the list below, pick the things that take practice. Write them on your paper.

laughing	hitting a ball	jumping rope
sleeping	riding a bike	drinking

C. Exploring Language

The boy in the picture is roller-skating. What are some sports you have tried? Make a list of sports you have tried. Write on your paper.

Sports I Have Tried

_____

_____

_____

After you have listed some sports, finish the following sentences.

The hardest sport I ever tried was ____ .
It took me a ____ time to learn. I felt ____ when I first started to learn this sport.

D. Expressing Yourself

Draw a picture of someone learning a new sport. Have your classmates make up their own stories from what they see in the picture.